5

e

g

6

f

8

7

h

Answers on page 64

3

Into the Wood

The snow fell fast and the wind blew wild.
Into the wood went the Gruffalo's Child.

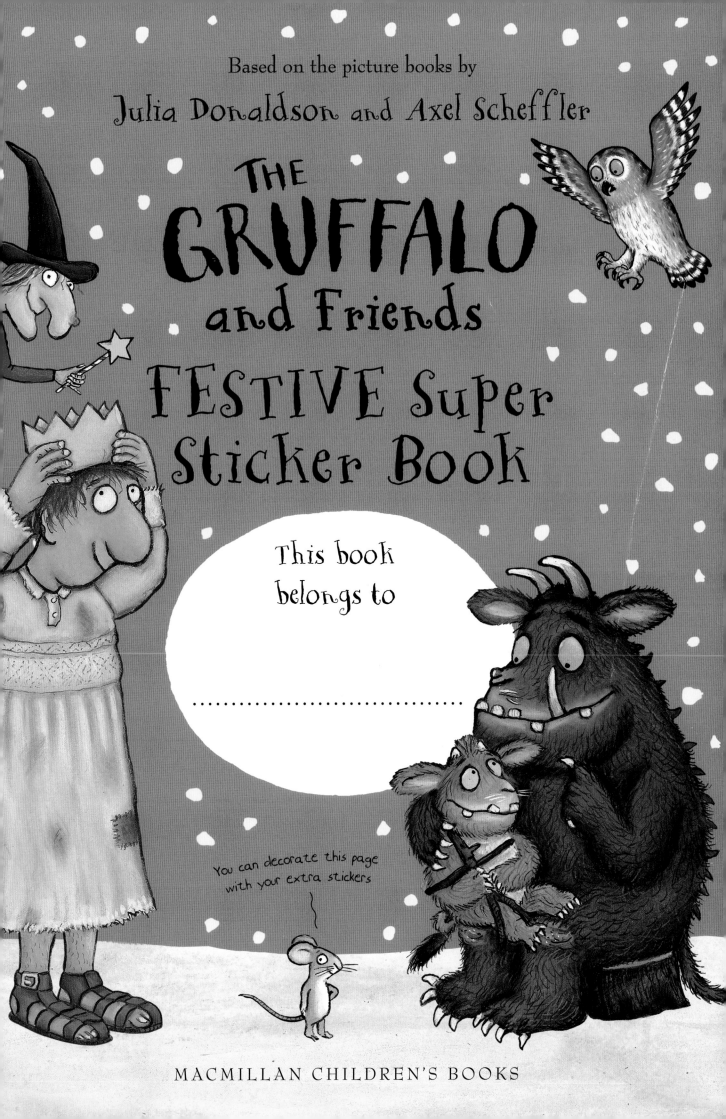

Based on the picture books by

Julia Donaldson and Axel Scheffler

THE GRUFFALO and Friends

FESTIVE Super Sticker Book

This book belongs to

....

You can decorate this page with your extra stickers

MACMILLAN CHILDREN'S BOOKS

Story Match

Oh help! Oh no! It's a Gruffalo!

But which book does he come from? Find the missing stickers, and then draw a line from each of the other characters to their stories.

We've done the first one for you!

1. THE GRUFFALO — JULIA DONALDSON · AXEL SCHEFFLER

2. The Snail and the Whale — JULIA DONALDSON · AXEL SCHEFFLER

3. Charlie Cook's Favourite Book — JULIA DONALDSON · AXEL SCHEFFLER

4.

a

b

c

d

Use your square jigsaw stickers to complete the picture.

Towering Icebergs

The snail and the whale sail past icy lands.
Use your stickers to cover this iceberg with penguins.

 What else can you add to the scene?

Broomstick Ride

Colour in this picture of the witch and her cat flying through the air.
Then use your stickers to add lots of leaves blowing in the wind.

Deep Dark Wood Sticker Scene

A mouse took a stroll through the deep dark wood . . .

Who lives here? Use your stickers to fill the wood.

Don't forget to add Mouse!

Charlie Cook's Cosy Armchair

Charlie Cook is reading a book about pirates.
Can you spot ten differences between these two pictures?

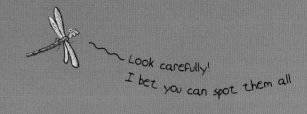

Look carefully!
I bet you can spot them all

Now use your stickers to make
the two pictures match.

Jungle Jokes!

Reward every good joke with a star sticker
– and every bad joke with a grumpy bat.

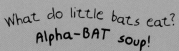
What do little bats eat?
Alpha-BAT soup!

RATE IT!

What do you get if you cross an elephant with a fish?
Swimming trunks!

RATE IT!

What is a crocodile's favourite game?
Snap!

RATE IT!

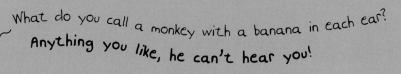
What do you call a monkey with a banana in each ear?
Anything you like, he can't hear you!

RATE IT!

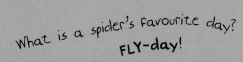
What is a spider's favourite day?
FLY-day!

RATE IT!

Monkey's Puzzles

Look at the three patterns below, then use your stickers to complete each one.

My House is a Squash and a Squeeze

How many things can you fit in the little old lady's house?
You can draw them in or use your stickers.

What would you put in your house?

You could draw lots of animals

The Smartest Giant Goes to Town

Can you help George find his way through the maze to town?
Sticker the characters as you pass them.

Windy Day Sticker Scene

The witch laughed aloud and held onto her hat,
But away blew the bow from her long ginger plait!

Use your stickers to complete the picture of the witch flying with her friends.
Don't forget the witch's bow flying away in the wind.

Add lots of leaves whirling around to show how windy it is

A Gruffalo! What's a Gruffalo?

Mouse scares off the animals by telling them about the Gruffalo.
Match your stickers to the descriptions.

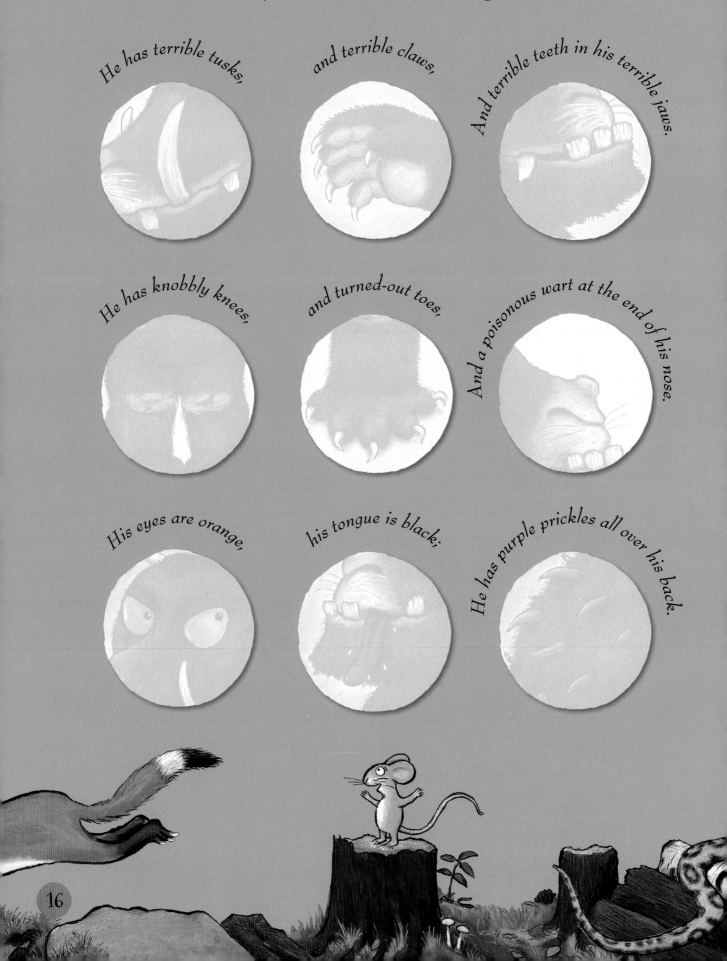

He has terrible tusks,

and terrible claws,

And terrible teeth in his terrible jaws.

He has knobbly knees,

and turned-out toes,

And a poisonous wart at the end of his nose.

His eyes are orange,

his tongue is black;

He has purple prickles all over his back.

16

What Comes Next?

The Gruffalo's Child meets lots of animals in the deep dark wood.
Use your stickers to complete the pattern on each row.

I really like doing these!

Me too

Spot the Difference Sticker Game

This is the whale who came one night
When the tide was high and the stars were bright.

Now use your stickers to make the picture below match the one above.

Can you spot ten differences between these two scenes?

Count them up — did you find ten?

If you get stuck, check your sticker page!

Aha! Oho! A Trail in the Snow!

Use the grid to help you draw Snake, then colour him in.

Owl's Treetop House

Search the sticker pages for other animals that live in trees.
Add them to the picture and then colour it in.

Draw some snow in the sky!

Charlie Cook's Books

Here are all of Charlie Cook's favourite books, but their spines
are looking a little bare. Find the missing pictures on
your sticker page and match them to the right shadows.

SHIVER ME TIMBERS

FAIRY TALES
FROM A FORGOTTEN ISLAND

THE BEANO ANNUAL

JOUST JOKING!

INCREDIBLE STORIES OF REAL BIRDS

Which book would you like to read the most?

A COUNTRY CHILDHOOD

IMPROVING STORIES FOR WICKED THIEVES

My First Encyclopedia

a
r
s
p
c
e
b
u
c
z

A-Z

OUT OF THIS WORLD
A COLLECTION OF GHOST STORIES

That's Not My Mum!

Butterfly takes Monkey to meet many creatures, but none of them is his real mum. Can you find the right stickers to match the descriptions?

 Good luck!

"My mum isn't a great grey hunk. She hasn't got tusks or a curly trunk."

"Mum doesn't look a bit like this. She doesn't slither about and hiss."

"Butterfly, Butterfly, please don't joke! Mum's not green and she doesn't croak."

"Mum's got a nose and not a beak. She doesn't squawk and squabble and shriek."

"Mum isn't black and hairy and fat. She's not got so many legs as that!"

"Why do you keep on getting it wrong? Mum doesn't sleep the whole day long."

24

The Cow Does a Jig

Well, the cow took one look and jumped straight at the pig,
Then jumped on the table and tapped out a jig.

Match your stickers to the right shadows to complete the picture.

Oh no! There goes the teapot . . .

Who Found the Wand?

The witch clutched her bow but let go of her wand. Oh no! Use your square stickers to complete the jigsaws and discover who found it in the pond.

The wand got very wet!

Is there room on the broom for the witch's new friend?

Mouse Meets Fox

Fox runs away when Mouse tells him about the Gruffalo.
Can you spot ten differences between these two pictures?

Now use your stickers to make this picture match the one above.

If you get stuck,
look on your sticker
page for a hint

Hide and Seek

The snow fell fast and the wind blew wild.
"I'm not scared," said the Gruffalo's Child.
There are ten creatures watching the Gruffalo's Child in the deep dark wood.
Find the missing stickers and see if you can spot them all!

A Snow Gruffalo

Mouse has been playing in the snow.
Join the dots to finish Mouse's snow gruffalo.

The Kindest Giant in Town

George helps all the animals by giving away his clothes. What did he give the goat whose sail blew away? Find it on your sticker page!

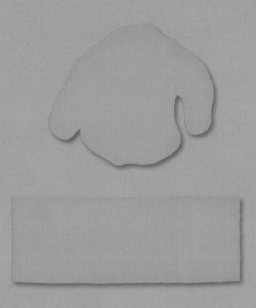

Use your stickers to show how many mice lived in George's shoe after their house burned down.

The Big Bad Mouse

The Gruffalo's Child has been looking for the Big Bad Mouse.
Finish the drawings below and colour them in.

The Big Bad Mouse is terribly strong

And his scaly tail is terribly long.

His eyes are like pools of terrible fire

And his terrible whiskers are tougher than wire.

Now decorate the page with lots of nuts for the Big Bad Mouse

31

The Wicked Jewel Thief

Charlie Cook reads a story about a jewel thief who stole the King's crown.
Match your stickers to the right shadows to complete the picture.

Now use your stickers to complete the pattern on each row.

Who Lives Here?

Lots of creatures live in the deep dark wood.
Look on your sticker page to find out who might live . . .

in a logpile house.

in an underground
house.

in a treetop house.

in the pond.

in the sky.

on the ground.

A Dragon!

"I am a dragon, as mean as can be!"
Colour in the mean dragon and draw lots of flames
coming out of his mouth. You can use your stickers too.

What a scary dragon!

I don't like it

Lots of Mud!

The witch's friends are covered in mud! Use your stickers
to add lots of muddy drops to the picture.

I think the animals might need a wash . . .

Look at all that mud!

Who was hiding under all that mud?
Find them on your sticker page and match them to the right shadows.

The Coldest Giant in Town

George's trousers have fallen down!
Find the missing stickers. Then search the scene for
the things below. Tick the boxes as you find them.

1 shoe ☐

2 birds ☐

3 bears ☐

4 dragonflies ☐

5 snails ☐

6 butterflies ☐

7 dwarfs ☐

Oh Help! Oh No!

It's a gruffalo!

Use your stickers to fill the deep dark wood with animals.
Are they scared of the Gruffalo?

Who Is This Creature?

Out came the moon. It was bright and round.
A terrible shadow fell onto the ground.

Can you draw Mouse's enormous shadow on the ground and then colour in the picture? Use your stickers to make the scene truly snowy.

An Empty Larder

"Even the pig in the larder agrees
My house is a squash and a squeeze."
Use your stickers to fill the larder with food.
Don't forget to put some food on the floor, too. What a mess!

Thank You, George!

George, the smartest giant in town,
won't stop until he's helped all the animals.

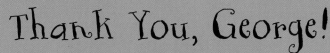

What fun!

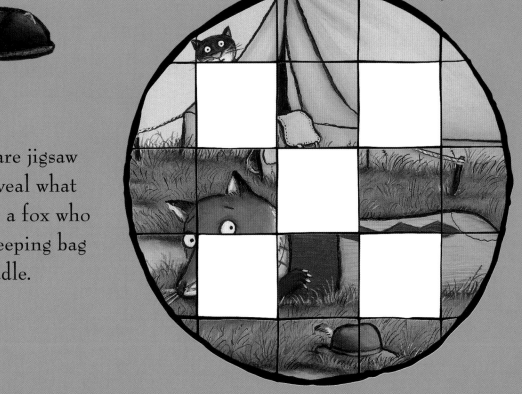

Use your square jigsaw
stickers to reveal what
George gave to a fox who
dropped his sleeping bag
in a puddle.

What did George give to the dog who was stuck in a bog?
Sticker to find out!

Are You Scared of the Gruffalo?

Who is running away from the Gruffalo?
Use your stickers to complete the scene and find out.

Spot the Difference Sticker Game

Can you spot ten differences between these two pictures
of the Gruffalo's Child ?

Now use your stickers
to make them match.

Your sticker page has a big clue to what's different

Marvellous Mountains

The snail and the whale see mountains and bears. Use your square jigsaw stickers to complete the picture.

Library Trails

One of the jokes in Charlie Cook's books was about a very well-read frog called Rowena Reddalot. Help her find her way to the library by following the lines.

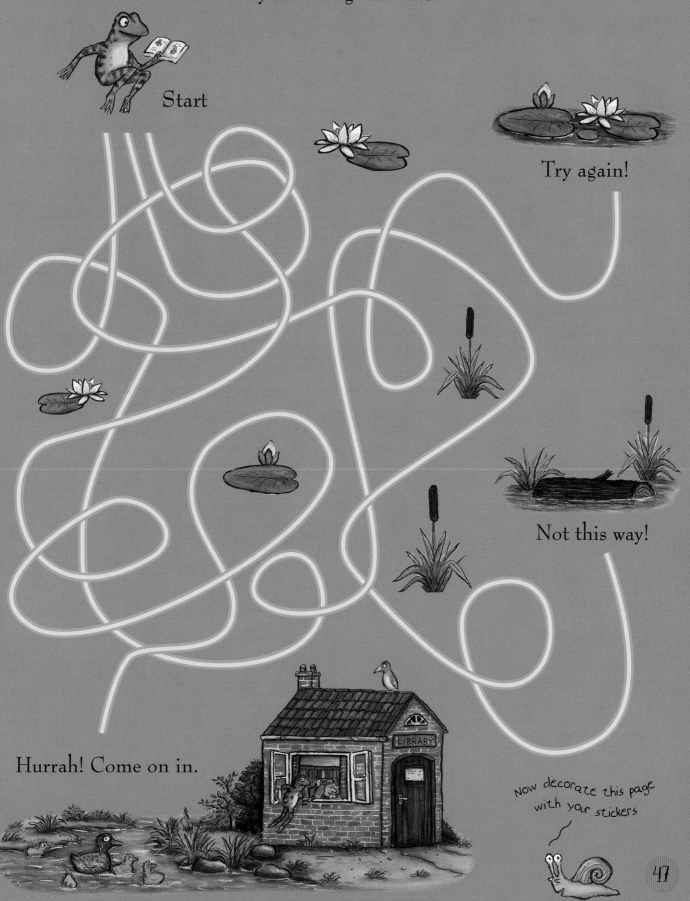

Start

Try again!

Not this way!

Hurrah! Come on in.

Now decorate this page with your stickers

A Magic Spell

"Find something, everyone, throw something in!"
What did the animals find to put in the cauldron?
Use your stickers to complete the jigsaw and find out!

What would you throw in? Draw some things in the circles below.
Then have a look on your sticker page and see if there is
anything else you can add to the cauldron!

Now stick the witch's wand in the cauldron to give everything a good stir

Design a Broomstick

If you could have your very own magnificent broom, what would it look like? Draw it below.

I don't need a broom to fly, but I'd still like one like that!

That's a Spider!

Butterfly still hasn't found Monkey's mum!
How many flies can you add to the spider's web?

Eeeeew! Poor flies

How many legs does a spider have?

Sticker Shadows

The Gruffalo's Child runs away from the Big Bad Mouse.
Use your stickers to complete the picture.

Can You Help Me Please?

"Take them all out," said the wise old man.
"But then I'll be back where I first began."
Use your stickers to complete the jigsaw.

Utter Chaos!

Find the missing stickers and add them to the page. Then, follow the lines to see which animal broke the teapot in the little old lady's house.

53

Who Found What?

The animals helped the witch find her missing things. Can you remember who found what? Stick the right object next to each animal.

Complete the Picture

The witch has got all her things back, hurrah! Now find each of her animal friends a wand, a hat, a broom and a bow on the sticker pages.

And They All Set Sail . . .

Colour in this picture of the snails going on a new adventure with the whale.
How many snail stickers can you add to the whale's tail?

What colour will the sky be?

Is it a sunny day?

Charlie Cook's Wordsearch

Can you find these eight words in the grid below?
Words can go across or down.

FROG ALIEN BOOK BIRD

PIRATE GHOST CAKE DRAGON

B	O	O	K	E	R	F	L
I	G	B	O	C	D	B	B
R	P	I	R	A	T	E	L
D	F	T	K	K	X	L	A
T	R	O	C	E	D	E	L
S	O	G	H	O	S	T	I
F	G	R	W	S	A	I	E
R	F	D	R	A	G	O	N

Monkey Maze

Can you guide Monkey through the maze and help him find his mum?
Then add the missing animals with your stickers.

Then use your extra stickers to decorate the page!

Goodbye, Gruffalo!

Colour in the picture of the Gruffalo running away.

A Nut for Mouse

Hurrah for Mouse! Can you find a nut for him on your sticker page?
Now see what else you can add to the picture.

The Kindest Giant

Can you colour in the picture and draw a crown on George's head?

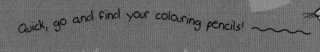
Quick, go and find your colouring pencils!

A Letter for George

Use your stickers to fill in the blanks below.

Your tie is a ___
for a cold giraffe,
Your shirt's on a boat

as a sail for a ___
Your shoe is a house
for a little white ___

One of your socks
is a bed for a ___,
Your belt helped a dog, who was

crossing a ___,
So here is a very
fine crown,

to go with the sandals and gown
of the ___ giant in town.

If you got them all right, place a sticker
crown on this drawing of George.

The Gruffalo Cave

The Gruffalo's Child was a bit less bored . . .
And the Gruffalo snored and snored and snored.

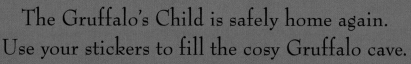

What can you add outside the cave?

The Gruffalo's Child is safely home again.
Use your stickers to fill the cosy Gruffalo cave.

Answers

Pages 2-3: Story Match
1: a, 2: f, 3: e, 4: h, 5: b, 6: d, 7: g, 8: c

Page 13: The Smartest Giant Goes to Town

Pages 36-37: The Coldest Giant in Town

Page 47: Library Trails

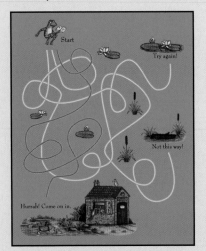

Page 53: Utter Chaos!

Page 56: Charlie Cook's Wordsearch

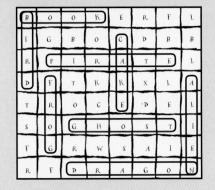

Page 57: Monkey Maze

Page 61: A Letter for George

Pages 2-3 Story Match

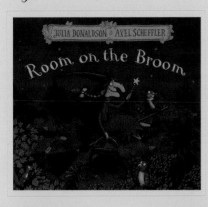

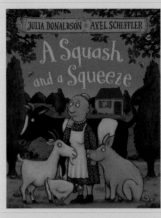

Pages 4-5 Into the Wood

Page 6 Towering Icebergs

Extra Stickers

Page 7 Broomstick Ride

Pages 8–9 Deep Dark Wood Sticker Scene

Page 10 Charlie Cook's Cosy Armchair

Page 11 Jungle Jokes!

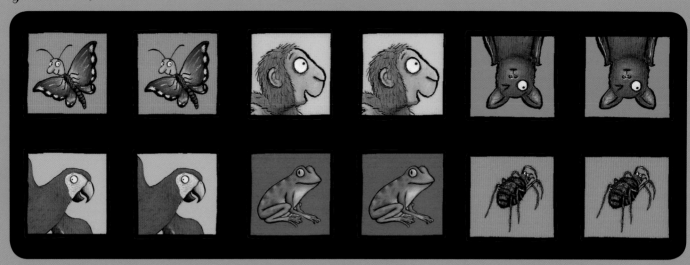

Page 12 My House is a Squash and a Squeeze

Page 13 The Smartest Giant Goes to Town

Extra Stickers

Pages 14–15 Windy Day Sticker Scene

Page 16 A Gruffalo! What's a Gruffalo?

Page 17 What Comes Next?

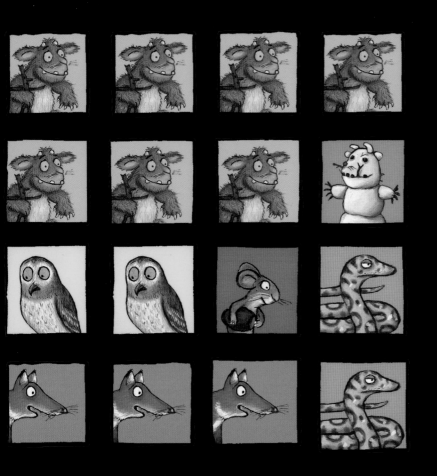

Pages 18–19 Spot the Difference
Sticker Game

Extra Stickers

Page 21 Owl's Treetop House

Pages 22–23 Charlie Cook's Books

Page 24 That's Not My Mum!

Page 25 The Cow Does a Jig

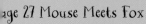

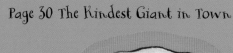

SHIRT

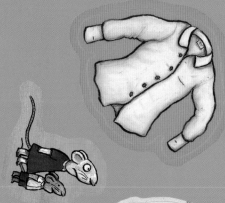

Page 32 The Wicked Jewel Thief

Page 33 Who Lives Here?

Page 34 A Dragon!

Page 35 Lots of Mud!

Page 42 An Empty Larder

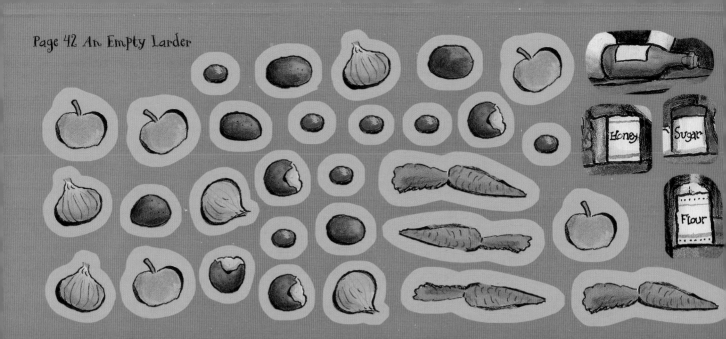

Page 43 Thank You, George!

BELT

Page 44 Are You Scared of the Gruffalo?

Page 45 Spot the Difference Sticker Game

Page 46 Marvellous Mountains

Page 47 Library Trails

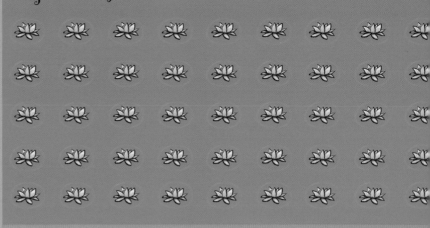

Page 48 A Magic Spell

Page 50 That's a Spider!

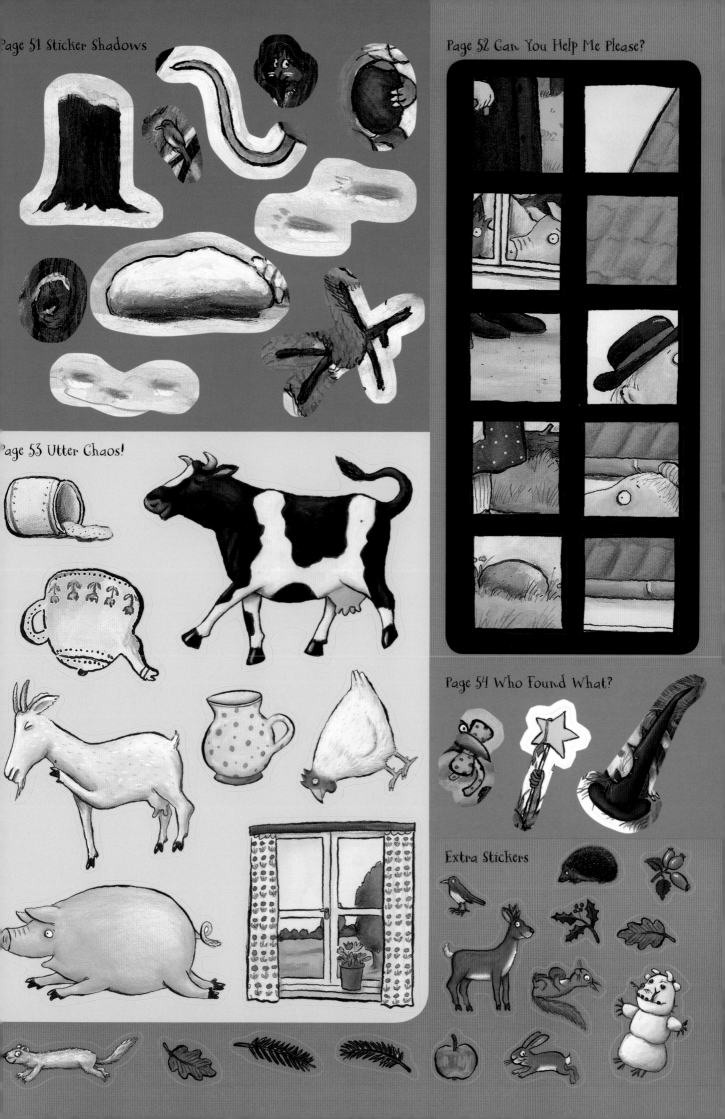

Page 51 Sticker Shadows

Page 52 Can You Help Me Please?

Page 53 Utter Chaos!

Page 54 Who Found What?

Extra Stickers

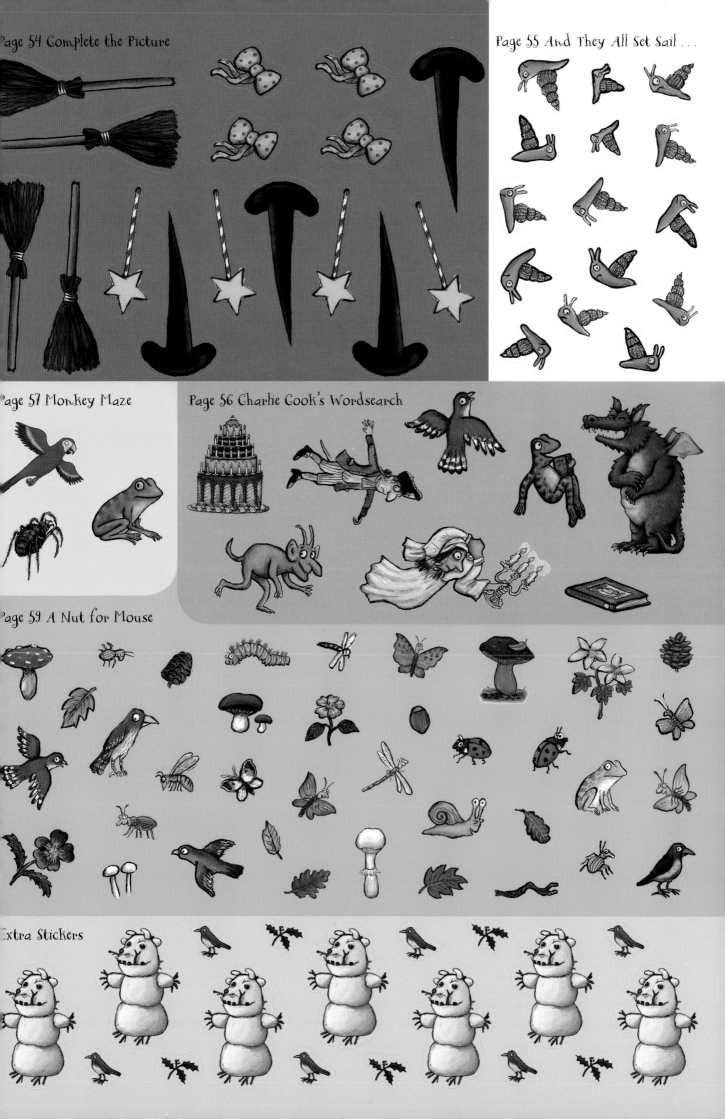

Page 54 Complete the Picture

Page 55 And They All Set Sail . . .

Page 57 Monkey Maze

Page 56 Charlie Cook's Wordsearch

Page 59 A Nut for Mouse

Extra Stickers

KINDEST   scarf   Fox bog mouse   goat

ages 62-63 The Gruffalo Cave